i-SPY

CW01024405

# Cars

## SPY IT! SCORE IT!

# Introduction

Car manufacturers produce many different models in a variety of shapes, sizes and styles. Some you may have heard of before and some will be unfamiliar. New models are introduced throughout the year, so you will undoubtedly spot vehicles not in this book while spotting our selection.

*i-SPY cars* covers a cross-section of cars seen on British roads, from popular mass-production models to high-performance luxury supercars, off-roaders to people carriers and classics to ultra-modern hybrid electric cars. There really is a car for everyone in this book.

## How to use your i-SPY book

Keep your eyes peeled for the i-SPYs in the book.

If you spy it, score it by ticking the circle or star.

Items with a star are difficult to spot so you'll have to search high and low to find them.

Once you score 1000 points, send away for your super i-SPY certificate. Follow the instructions on page 64 to find out how.

The ALFA (Anonima Lombarda Fabbrica Automobili) company was formed in 1910 and was changed to Alfa Romeo in 1920. In 1923 a young racing driver named Enzo Ferrari joined Alfa Romeo and would later run their racing team before leaving to design and manufacture cars under his own name. Alfa Romeo is now under the ownership of Fiat Chrysler. Often referred to as Alfa, it has a rich history in motor racing throughout the first part of the last century and has had victories in many races.

## MiTo

**10 POINTS**

## Giulietta

**10 POINTS**

# Alfa Romeo

## GT

**10** POINTS

## Brera

**10** POINTS

## 4C

**20** POINTS

Audi can trace its origin back to 1899 but became a major car producer when four German carmakers – Audi, Horch, DKW and Wanderer – merged to form Auto Union in 1932. It is now part of the Volkswagen Group along with other makes like Bentley, VW, SEAT and Škoda and is seen as an upmarket and prestige brand. Look out for Audi's amazing R8 supercar that shares a platform and a V10 engine with the Lamborghini Gallardo. Take a special look at the Audi badge, with the four interlocking rings representing the four companies that merged to form Auto Union.

**A3**

**5 POINTS**

**A4**

**5 POINTS**

5

# Audi

## A5/A6/A7/A8

Score for any model from the Audi range of 'executive' saloons, and coupés.

**10 POINTS**

## TT

Score double points if you find a diesel version.

**10 POINTS**

## Q3/Q5/Q7

Score for any of Audi's SUVs.

**10 POINTS**

## R8

**TOP SPOT!**

**30 POINTS**

6

BMW – Bayerische Motoren Werke (Bavarian Motor Works) – was founded in 1916 primarily as a motorcycle and engine manufacturing company. After successfully making aircraft engines and motorcycles, BMW moved into car manufacturing and has had a remarkable transformation since the 1960s when it began to make high-quality mid-market saloons, as well as the luxury models it was known for. It now has the famous British names of Rolls-Royce and Mini within its group. Score double for any BMW with the blue and red M badge, denoting the high-performance version of a model.

## 1 Series/ 2 Series

The 2 Series is a coupé version of the 1 Series.

**5 POINTS**

## 3 Series/ 4 Series

The 4 Series is the coupé version of the 3 Series.

**5 POINTS**

## i3

Still hard to spot outside London, BMW's electric city car is one of the faster electric cars around.

**20 POINTS**

## X1/X3/ X5/X6

The X range of SUVs increase in size as the number increases. Score for any of BMW's 4x4s, but double for the more scarce X6.

**10 POINTS**

## 5 Series

**5 POINTS**

## 6 Series

**10 POINTS**

## 7 Series

**10 POINTS**

## z4

**15 POINTS**

9

**TOP SPOT!**

## i8

The highly innovative BMW i8 is a petrol-electric hybrid supercar that can go from 0–60 mph in just over four seconds. While electric cars become more commonplace on UK roads, spotting one of these electric supercars is still very rare.

**35 POINTS**

# Citroën

Founded by André Citroën in France in 1919, Citroën was the first mass-production car manufacturer outside the USA. . They are famous for the 2CV *(see Classic cars, page 60)* – a very simple, lightweight car developed to bring affordable transport to rural France, but it was so successful, however, that it remained in production around the world from 1948 to 1990. Since 1976 Citroën has been part of PSA Group, Peugeot Citroën Automobiles based in Paris, and in 2015 it rebadged its luxury cars to a separate brand – DS Automobiles.

## C-Zero

**15 POINTS**

## C1/C3

Score for either hatchback.

**5 POINTS**

## C3 Picasso/ C4 Picasso

Score for any Picasso-badged MPV.

**5 POINTS**

# Dacia

This Romanian firm has been owned by Renault since 1999 but it's only in more recent years that imports to the UK have risen sharply. Dacia offers some of the least expensive cars in the UK and promotes their value for money.

## Sandero

**10** POINTS

## Logan

**15** POINTS

## Duster

**10** POINTS

The DS range are upmarket Citroëns, but they don't carry the Citroën name or even the double-chevron badge. The DS3 and DS4 share much with the Citroën C3 and C4, but the 5 is now a DS-only model.

### DS3

**10 POINTS**

### DS4

The semi-SUV Crossback (shown) sits slightly higher than the standard model. Score for any DS4.

**10 POINTS**

### DS5

**15 POINTS**

# Fiat

Fiat is an Italian manufacturer of all kinds of vehicles including cars and trucks, and is now amalgamated with Chrysler. It also owns Alfa Romeo and Maserati, and is heavily involved in motor racing. There was a very famous model called the Cinquecento or Fiat 500, a simple rear-engined runabout with a tiny 500cc engine that became very fashionable as a classic. The model was reinvented and its range has grown to include cars far larger than the original 500.

## 500 (new)

Score double points if you find a white one with green and red stripes. These are the colours of the Italian flag.

 **5** POINTS

## Panda

 **10** POINTS

## Punto

**10**
POINTS

## 500L MPW

A seven-seat MPV
wearing the old
500's name badge.

**20**
POINTS

## Qubo/Doblo

Score for either of
Fiat's van-based
MPVs.

**10**
POINTS

# Ford

The Ford Motor Company of America was started in 1903. Its founder, Henry Ford once famously said, 'You can have any colour of car you like, as long as it's black'. This remark referred to the company's famous Model T, which was the first mass market car produced on an assembly line, a method that was to transform the manufacture of cars. Henry Ford's vision changed car production forever and would be copied by all volume carmakers around the world. Today Ford has factories worldwide and has been in continuous family control for over 100 years.

## Ka

**5 POINTS**

## Fiesta

**5 POINTS**

## Focus

 **5 POINTS**

## Mondeo

 **5 POINTS**

## B-MAX/C-MAX/ S-MAX

Score for any of Ford's MPV family.

 **10 POINTS**

**TOP SPOT!**

## Mustang

Ford's legendary muscle car is now imported to the UK in right-hand drive.

 **30 POINTS**

# Honda

Honda of Japan started life as motorcycle makers and still sell millions of motorcycles all over the world. In the 1960s they started to make small-engined motor cars – their first had chain-driven rear wheels using almost the same technology used in motorcycles. Honda is relatively new as a maker, only starting manufacturing after World War II, and like others, has demonstrated its products through racing both motorcycles and cars in competitions, including Formula One.

## Jazz

**5** POINTS

## Civic

**5** POINTS

## HR-V/CR-V

Score for either of Honda's crossover SUVs.

**10** POINTS

Hyundai started life in the construction business in 1947 and became South Korea's largest industrial company. The Hyundai Motor Company's first global success came from their Pony model. It was particularly successful in the USA in the 1980s as American motorists came to value the economy offered by cars from the Far East.

## i20

**10** POINTS

## i40

**10** POINTS

## Santa Fe/ Tucson

Score for either Hyundai 4x4.

**10** POINTS

19

# Infiniti

Nissan's luxury division started selling cars in America in 1989 but the arrival in the UK and its home market, Japan, was much more recent. Some models have been produced at Nissan UK's plant in Sunderland, including the Q30 hatchback launched in late 2015, though there are plans to stop selling this brand in Western Europe.

## Q30

**10 POINTS**

## Q50/Q70

Score for either Infiniti saloon.

**15 POINTS**

## QX50/QX70

Score for either SUV.

**20 POINTS**

Jaguar is a famous British marque with a long history of making sports cars and sporting saloons. Its most celebrated car was the E-type *(see Classic Cars, page 61)*, which every subsequent Jaguar sports car has had to live up to. The exciting F-type is the latest Jaguar to wear the E-type's crown, but the newest Jaguar – the F-PACE – is a daring move into the SUV market.

## F-type

**15 POINTS**

## XE/XF/XJ

Score for any of the four-door Jaguar saloons.

**10 POINTS**

## F-PACE

**20 POINTS**

# Jeep

The first Jeep was a famous 4x4 vehicle chosen by the US Army to move quickly over difficult terrain. From the early days of military vehicles, the companies behind the Jeep brand – it's changed hands a few times – have used its reputation of strength and reliability to form the basis of an evermore refined range, though toughness and off-road prowess are still important.

## Renegade

**15** POINTS

## Wrangler

**10** POINTS

## Cherokee

**10** POINTS

South Korean company Kia, was founded in 1944 as a manufacturer of steel tubing and bicycles. It later went on to build motorcycles, trucks and cars. In the past Kia have helped Mazda and Ford develop and produce cars for local markets; this is a perfect example of how manufacturers who normally compete as rivals cooperate with each other in order to enter certain markets and reduce their costs.

## Venga/Carens

Score for either of Kia's MPVs.

**10** POINTS

## Sportage

**5** POINTS

## Ceed/ ProCeed

Score for any of this similar family of hatches and small estates.

**10** POINTS

23

# Land Rover

Land Rover is probably the most famous off-road vehicle in the world. This British brand originated as a single, Jeep-like model developed by the Rover company, which stopped making cars in 2005. By then, Land Rover had been a separate business for some time, having developed more luxurious and versatile vehicles. Land Rover was bought by the Indian company Tata Motors in 2008. The basic Defender model, which had changed relatively little from the 1948 original, stopped production in 2016, though a new Defender has recently been launched.

## Range Rover

Score 15 for the sleeker Range Rover Sport.

**10 POINTS**

## Discovery Sport

Replacement for the popular Freelander model, which was produced between 1997 and 2014.

**15 POINTS**

## Discovery

**5** POINTS

## Defender

**15** POINTS

## Range Rover Evoque

**10** POINTS

## Range Rover Evoque Convertible

A soft-top soft-roader!

**25** POINTS

# Lexus

Lexus is the luxury brand of Toyota, and makes cars to compete with the other high-end companies such as Mercedes, BMW and Audi. Lexus is a good example of a major manufacturer creating a new brand to compete in another segment of the market that they would not normally be able to enter. Score double points if you spot a car with an 'h' badge, indicating the hybrid power systems optional on most Lexus models.

**LS**

10 POINTS

**GS**

10 POINTS

**CT**

10 POINTS

**IS**

**10 POINTS**

**RC-F**

**25 POINTS**

**RX**

**15 POINTS**

# Mazda

Mazda is famous for using the Wankel rotary engine in its vehicles, first introduced in 1967 as a powerful, compact alternative to conventional piston engines. Other carmakers abandoned this design due to challenges with economy and reliability, but Mazda continued offering the Wankel until 2012.

## Mazda2

**10** POINTS

## Mazda3

**10** POINTS

## Mazda6

**10** POINTS

## CX-3

**10 POINTS**

## CX-5

**10 POINTS**

## MX-5

**15 POINTS**

# Mercedes-Benz

Germany's Mercedes-Benz is one of the most prestigious carmakers in the world, with an instantly recognisable three-pointed star for a badge. The Mercedes AMG Petronas Formula One team has been winning the World Championship for Constructors since 2014. Today, Mercedes makes a vast range of cars from small city cars to, luxury 4x4s and sports coupés, plus everything in between. The AMG badge is equivalent to BMW's M badge: score double when you see this.

## A-Class/ B-Class

Score for either of these hatchbacks.

**10 POINTS**

## C-Class

Both this and the E-Class have two-door coupé versions – score double for these.

**10 POINTS**

## E-Class

**15** POINTS

## SL/SLK

Score for either of the two-seat Mercedes. The SL is the big brother.

**15** POINTS

## CLA/CLS

Coupé equivalents of the C- and E-Class, but still with four doors. Also in estate form.

**15** POINTS

## S-Class

**15** POINTS

# Mercedes-Benz

## GLA/GLC/GLE/GLS/G

Mercedes also have a range of chunky SUVs although they are not as familiar a sight on UK roads as their BMW or Audi equivalents. The GLA and GLC are at the smaller end of the range, while the GLE and GLS are more spacious. The permanently four-wheel-drive G is a serious off-roader. Score for any Mercedes SUV.

**20** POINTS

The BMC Mini was first made in 1959 and was an instant hit. At the time it was revolutionary, adopting a new front-wheel-drive engine and gearbox which was mounted transversely between the front wheels, enabling the car to be made smaller while remaining as roomy as previous models. The Mini has become iconic over the years and although now owned by Germany's BMW, many of the cars that wear a Mini badge are still made in Oxford. Look out for the designs that customise the Mini, many of which incorporate the Union Flag.

## Hatch

 **10 POINTS**

Watch out for the Cooper models and special editions.

## Clubman

**15 POINTS**

## Countryman

 **10 POINTS**

Score double if you see this or the Clubman parked next to the tiny original Mini.

33

# Mitsubishi

The Mitsubishi Company was founded in 1870 as a shipping firm. Car manufacture is just one part of this huge corporation. Since 1970, when the car company was formed, Chrysler, the US carmaker, had an interest in the company. Mitsubishi is now part of an alliance with Renault and Nissan.

## Outlander

Score double for hybrid PHEV version.

**10** POINTS

## ASX

**10** POINTS

## Shogun

**10** POINTS

# Nissan

Nissan formerly sold cars under the Datsun name and was one of the first Japanese makers to sell cars in any volume in the UK with their small car, called the Datsun Cherry. Very quickly they established a good name in reliability and value for money. They are now one of the major global manufacturers and have a close alliance with the French car manufacturer Renault.

## Micra

**10 POINTS**

## Note

**5 POINTS**

## Leaf

**25 POINTS**

# Nissan

## Juke

 **10 POINTS**

## Qashqai

 **10 POINTS**

## X-Trail

 **10 POINTS**

## 370Z

 **25 POINTS**

Peugeot's roots go back to a family business that was founded in 1810. In 1858 the Peugeot family filed its trademark lion and in 1889 produced its first automobile. Today Peugeot have a particular reputation in designing efficient diesel engines, and an excellent history in off-road rallying, including the famous Monte Carlo Rally. In 1976 Peugeot and Citroën merged into one company to form PSA Peugeot Citroën (now known as PSA Group), based in Paris.

## 108

**5 POINTS**

## 208

**5 POINTS**

# Peugeot

## 308

 **10 POINTS**

## 508

 **15 POINTS**

## 3008

Score the same for the 2008 hatch and 5008 MPV.

 **10 POINTS**

## RCZ

Peugeot's take on the Audi TT concept has been a hit.

 **20 POINTS**

Founded in 1930 by Ferdinand Porsche, the company did not initially manufacture cars but was a consulting firm offering services to companies developing motor vehicles. The first model under the Porsche name was the Porsche 64, produced in 1939. Porsche's most famous model, the 911, has been updated many times since 1963 but still retains the same overall shape and a rear-mounted, flat-six engine. More recently, Porsche has launched saloon and SUV models.

## Boxster

**15** POINTS

## Cayman

**25** POINTS

# Porsche

## Macan

**20** POINTS

## Cayenne

**10** POINTS

## Panamera

**25** POINTS

## 911

The 911 is one of the most iconic supercars of all time. The first model was built in 1963, and since then each new version of the 911 has managed to combine beautiful curved lines with blistering performance. This combination has meant that the car is as well known for its success in rallying and track competition, as well as its head turning ability on a country road or city street. Spotting one is always a pleasure.

**30 POINTS**

# Renault

The Renault brothers (Louis, Marcel and Fernand) together with two of their friends began producing cars in 1897 and sold their first Voiturette 1CV (meaning one horsepower) in 1898. Two years later the Renault Corporation was founded as 'Société Renault Frères'. They have been prominent in motor racing across Europe at the very highest levels, including Formula One. At the other end of the scale, a popular race championship for the Clio hatchback takes place in the UK.

## Twizy/ZOE

Renault's zero-emissions vehicles: Twizy is an eccentric micro-car (right), while ZOE looks like a traditional hatchback. Score for either.

**20 POINTS**

## Twingo

**10 POINTS**

## Captur

 **10** POINTS

## Clio

**10** POINTS

## Mégane

 **5** POINTS

## Scenic/ Grand Scenic

 **10** POINTS

# SEAT

SEAT (Sociedad Española de Automóviles de Turismo) was founded in Spain in 1950, initially with assistance from Group Fiat. The SEAT 600, based on the Fiat 600, was the first mass-produced car to be owned by many Spanish families. The collaboration with Fiat ended in 1981 and after producing cars independently, the company began a partnership with Audi/VW in 1986, which resulted in the integration of SEAT into the Volkswagen Group.

## Ibiza

**5** POINTS

## Leon
Score double for the super-quick Cupra model.

**5** POINTS

## Ateca

**20** POINTS

Škoda is a car manufacturer based in Czechia, which became a subsidiary of the Volkswagen Group in 1991. The origins of Škoda go back to the mid-1890s when the company started out manufacturing bicycles. In 1899 their first motorcycle appeared and by 1905 the first car was produced. In 1924, after running into difficulties, they sought a partner and merged with Škoda Works, the biggest industrial enterprise in Czechoslovakia at the time, and adopted their name. They previously made unconventional 'no-frills' cars, but since the VW Group has taken them over they have enhanced their reputation and now appeal to many more customers.

**Fabia** **10** POINTS

**10** POINTS **Yeti**

**Octavia**

**5** POINTS

**Superb**

**10** POINTS

# smart

Unusually for a car company, smart began as a design concept shared between Mercedes and a watch brand, Swatch. Volkswagen took over backing at one point before Mercedes launched the first smart fortwo in 1998. The name comes from an abbreviation of **S**watch **M**ercedes **ART** and the company is part of Daimler AG, like Mercedes. This type of car is particularly suited to those living and travelling in cities as it is very short in length and can be parked very easily.

## fortwo

Score double for a convertible.

 **10 POINTS**

## forfour

 **15 POINTS**

## roadster

**30 POINTS**

**TOP SPOT!**

Production stopped in the mid-2000s but a strong community of owners has kept a good number on the road.

# Subaru

Subaru is a Japanese maker that first entered the UK market selling cars to those who needed to drive in off-road terrain or on muddy, unmade tracks. Typical customers included farmers and people living in remote parts of the country, but Subaru's four-wheel-drive cars found much more success and credibility when the company turned to rallying, winning a total of five World Rally Championship titles.

## Forester

**10** POINTS

## BRZ

**20** POINTS

## Outback

**10** POINTS

# Suzuki

Suzuki was formed in 1909 to make weaving looms for the Japanese silk industry, and started making motor cars in 1937. After the end of World War II they developed small motorcycles as the demand for affordable transport grew in Japan. By 1952 Suzuki Motors was born. Today Suzuki is the ninth largest carmaker in the world as well as being one of the leading global motorcycle makers.

## Swift

**5** POINTS

## Celerio

**10** POINTS

## Vitara

**5** POINTS

Toyota is the largest motor car company in the world. In 1934 Toyota designed and built its first engine, followed in 1936 with the building of its first car. Toyota was another company to profit from the oil crisis in the US with increased sales of their economical smaller cars, which offered large fuel savings over the American cars of the day. This early success allowed Toyota to set up factories in America making cars designed specifically for the US domestic markets and also to build car plants in many other countries, including Britain.

## Aygo

**5** POINTS

## Yaris

**10** POINTS

# Toyota

## Prius

Toyota's ground-breaking Prius is now much improved.

**15** POINTS

## Avensis

**5** POINTS

## Land Cruiser

**10** POINTS

## GT 86

A collaboration with Subaru, but with Toyota's own engine not the Subaru flat-four.

**20** POINTS

Vauxhall is a very old British marque, first making cars in 1903. In 1925 it became part of the General Motors Corporation but despite much model-sharing with German GM brand Opel, it retained a strong British identity and manufacturing presence in Luton and Ellesmere Port, Cheshire. Since 2017 Vauxhall has been part of PSA Group, and continues to enjoy strong sales to company fleet customers.

## Viva

An old Vauxhall model name is revived.

## Adam

# Vauxhall

## Corsa

**5** POINTS

## Astra

**5** POINTS

## Meriva/Zafira

Score points for either of Vauxhall's MPVs.

**5** POINTS

## Mokka

**10** POINTS

# Volkswagen

Volkswagen arose from a badly-bombed car factory that had started to produce a 'people's car' under the direction of the German Third Reich in the 1930s. German citizens were encouraged to invest a small sum every week to save for a new car, but the money largely disappeared and few were delivered. Now Volkswagen has become an immensely successful group with many famous marques under its control, including Bentley, Bugatti, Lamborghini, Audi, SEAT and Škoda.

## Up!

**10 POINTS**

## Polo

**5 POINTS**

# Volkswagen

## Golf/Jetta

Score double for the Golf-based saloon, the Jetta.

 **5** POINTS

## Beetle (new)

 **15** POINTS

## Passat

 **5** POINTS

## Tiguan/Touareg

Score for either of VW's SUVs.

 **10** POINTS

Volvo is a Swedish carmaker with a strong reputation for making cars with excellent safety features. Like Saab, Volvo was very late in offering diesel engines in their cars due to the very cold conditions in their home market – diesel fuel can solidify in sub-zero Scandinavian winters. You will see many Volvo trucks on the roads that were originally part of the same company but are now independent following the sale of the car division to Ford in 2000. In 2010, Ford sold Volvo cars to a Chinese maker, Geely.

## V40/V60/V90

Score for any hatchback or estate.

**5 POINTS**

## S60/S90

Score for either saloon.

**10 POINTS**

## XC60/XC90

Score for either crossover SUV.

**10 POINTS**

# Supercars and luxury cars

### Aston Martin

James Bond's car of choice.

**20** POINTS

### Bentley

Hefty sports GTs and super-luxury saloons with a great British heritage, though now owned by VW.

TOP SPOT!

**35** POINTS

**50** POINTS

TOP SPOT!

### Bugatti

Every part of the Chiron, Bugatti's late supercar, is made as light as possible except for the solid silver Bugatti badge. That's why it has acceleration of 0–62 mph in 2.5 seconds and a limited top speed of 261 mph!

# Ferrari

Classic Italian sports cars founded by
Enzo Ferrari in 1928, which are now
part of the Fiat Group.

**30** POINTS

TOP
SPOT!

# Lamborghini

Lamborghini produce some of
the most powerful and expensive
sports cars seen on the roads.

**40** POINTS

TOP
SPOT!

# Supercars and luxury cars

## Lotus

British sports car manufacturer since 1952. Current models include the Elise and the Exige.

**20** POINTS

## Maserati

A range of luxury sports saloons and GTs benefiting from the same ownership as Ferrari.

**15** POINTS

**40** POINTS

## McLaren

F1 constructor now making road cars including the incredible 217 mph P1.

TOP SPOT!

## Pagani

Outdoing Ferrari and Lamborghini for exclusivity, the Huayra Roadster BC costs £3.7 million.

**40 POINTS**

## Rolls-Royce

'The best car in the world' was once the slogan, which could still be true of modern R-Rs.

**30 POINTS**

## Stretched limo

Mostly driven by chauffeurs as transport to parties and weddings. Many come with televisions, DVD players and bars as standard. Score double points for a pink one.

**15 POINTS**

# Classic cars

### AC Cobra

A brutal machine created by putting an American Ford V8 engine into a light British spo car, the AC Ace. Score half if it's only a replica.

**40** POINTS

**TOP SPOT!**

### BMC Mini

The original Mini was very popular so there are still quite a few around. Score double for one with a Union Jack on the roof.

**20** POINTS

**30** POINTS

### Citroën 2CV

Millions of these cheap and practical little cars were built between 1948 an 1990. In their day they were popular for their easy maintenance and soft ride, but spotting them on UK roads is getting pretty difficult nowadays.

**TOP SPOT!**

## Fiat 500 (original)

The original 'Cinquecento' (Italian for 500) was a tiny, twin-cylinder runabout that just about offered space for four people.

**25** POINTS

## Ford Capri

'The car you always promised yourself' said the advert, and the much-customised Capri became an object of desire for millions.

**TOP SPOT!**

**30** POINTS

## Jaguar E-type

Enzo Ferrari called it the most beautiful car in the world – quite a recommendation! Score for either roadster or coupé versions.

**25** POINTS

# Classic cars

## MGB

Britain's most popular classic sports car? It lasted in production for nearly 20 years and thousands are still on the road.

**20** POINTS

## Morris Minor

A huge post-war success story and the first British car to sell a million. Score double for a convertible or the cute, wood-framed Traveller.

**30** POINTS

**TOP SPOT!**

## VW Beetle (original)

The Beetle (or 'Bug' in North America, 'Käfer' in Germany) was an even greater success story than the Morris Minor. Score double for a convertible or a rare 'split screen' version.

**15** POINTS

# Index

# i-SPY

**How to get your i-SPY certificate and badge**

**Let us know when you've become a super-spotter with 1000 points and we'll send you a special certificate and badge!**

**Here's what to do:**

✓ Ask a grown-up to check your score.

✓ Apply for your certificate at www.collins.co.uk/i-SPY (if you are under the age of 13 we'll need a parent or guardian to do this).

✓ We'll email your certificate and post you a brilliant badge!